SUPERMARKET MAYHEM!

Naughty Evil Pea has made a huge mess in the toy aisle. Help Supertato tidy up by finding all the toys.

TEDDY BEAR

T-REX

CASTLE

HELICOPTER

VOLCANO

BOAT

CAR

BALL

Can you spot **Pea?**

*It's **EVIL** Pea!!!*

WHERE'S SUPERTATO?

ATTENTION, SUPER-VIEWERS! Where's Banana? He's hiding on **EVERY PAGE!**

A SEARCH-AND-FIND BOOK

Simon & Schuster
London New York Sydney Toronto New Delhi

SUPERTATO TO THE RESCUE!

Oh no! Evil Pea is up to no good in the supermarket. Can you find Supertato and his veggie friends so they can stop her sneaking into Tato Tower?

BROCCOLI   **CARROT**   **CHILLI**   **CORN COBS**

EVIL PEA   **SUPERTATO**   **TOMATO**

Supertato to the rescue!

With the help of his cape and Tato-belt, **Supertato** leaves no one behind!

LET'S PARTY!

Supertato loves a party!
Join in the fun by finding:

BROCCOLI   **CARROT**   **CHILLI**

SUPERTATO   **TOMATO**

CUPS   **BALLOONS**   **PRESENTS**

 How many party hats can you count?

I've got a plan!

Carrot is an acrobatic, super-smart sidekick and Supertato's best friend.

RUN, VEGGIES, RUN!

Evil Pea has covered the veggies with toilet roll. Can you save them all?

BROCCOLI **CARROT** **CHILLI**

SUPERTATO **TOMATO**

When you're done, try and spot Evil Pea hiding too.

EVIL PEA

Actually, I'm a fruit!

Super-squishy Tomato is a fearful but faithful friend to Supertato. He would also like you to know that he is a fruit not a veggie!

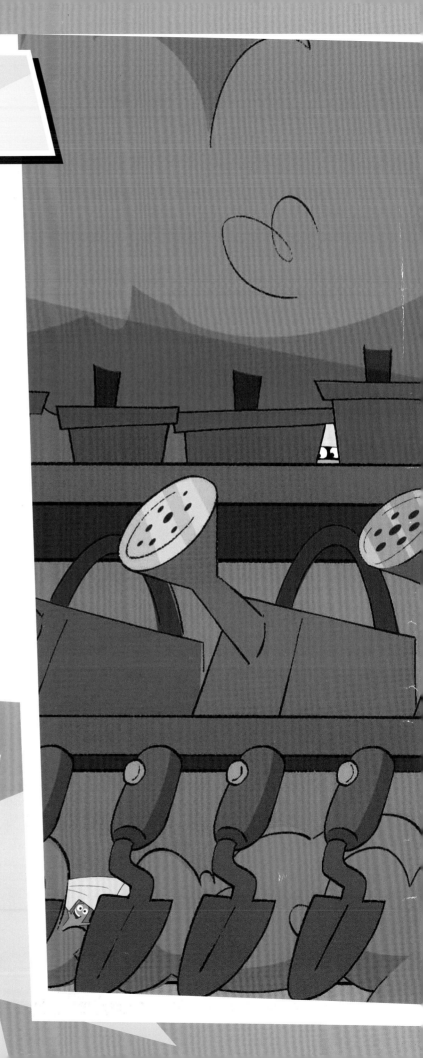

GAME ON!

The veggie friends love playing in the sports aisle. Who can you spot there?

BROCCOLI **CARROT** **CHILLI**

SUPERTATO **TOMATO** **CORN COBS**

SIX MINI PEAS

Can you spy sneaky **Evil Pea** trying to steal a ball?

PLANTS IN PERIL!

Oh dear, the plant shelf has got all muddled up.

Find Supertato and his friends so they can count each type of plant and tidy them up.

CARROT

SUPERTATO

BROCCOLI

PLANT 1　　　**PLANT 2**

PLANT 3

PLANT 4

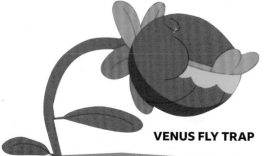
VENUS FLY TRAP

SUPER SPOTTER

Evil Pea has covered the supermarket in snow. Hip, hip, hurray it's a snow day! Everyone is playing hide-and-seek in the snow. Who can you spot?

BROCCOLI

CARROT

CHILLI

CORN COBS

EVIL PEA

SUPERTATO

TOMATO

SIX MINI PEAS

Once you've found everyone, see how many **spoons** you can find.

DELI DANCE-OFF

Evil Pea has challenged all the veggies to a dance-off in the deli. Can you spot everyone movin' and groovin'?

BROCCOLI **CARROT** **CHILLI** **CORN COBS**

EVIL PEA **SUPERTATO** **TOMATO**

SIX MINI PEAS

Can you
find the happy,
smiley **Mini Pea**?

SUPERMARKET SHOWDOWN

Supertato and his veggie friends are sneaking into Evil Pea's frozen lair . . . can you spot them?

BROCCOLI **CARROT** **CHILLI**

SUPERTATO **TOMATO**

Now try and spot the baddies too!

CORN COBS **EVIL PEA** **SIX MINI PEAS**

If you want a job done well, never ask Evil Pea's partners in crime, the very clumsy **Corn Cobs.**

SUPERMARKET SING-A-LONG

Help Supertato and his friends make music to sing and dance to by finding:

BROCCOLI

CARROT

CHILLI

SUPERTATO

TOMATO

5 UKULELES

10 YELLOW MUSIC NOTES

Who is lurking behind the xylophone?

It's time for the Broccoli Boogie!

Broccoli loves to dance and is always willing to give things a try.

DANGEROUS DOUGHNUTS

Yikes! Evil Pea has trapped the veggie friends. Can you spot them on the doughnut shelf?

BROCCOLI   **CARROT**   **CHILLI**

EVIL PEA   **SUPERTATO**   **TOMATO**

When you're done, can you find these sweet treats to reward them all with a **scrumptious snack**?

VEGGIES ASSEMBLE

Supertato needs his veggie friends for a mission, but one of them hasn't arrived yet.

Can you round them up and work out who is missing, then find them too?

CHILLI

BROCCOLI

SUPERTATO

TOMATO

Actually, I'm a fruit!

I am very not happy!

Chilli likes it when things go right, but stand back when things go wrong . . . as he gets hot!

THE BIG FREEZE

Brrrrr! Evil Pea has frozen all the veggies. How quickly can you find them?

BROCCOLI **CARROT** **CHILLI** **CORN COBS**

EVIL PEA **SUPERTATO** **TOMATO**

Can you spot
10 ice lollies
too?

TATO TOWER TAKEOVER

Uh-oh! Evil Pea has taken over Tato Tower. Help Supertato get rid of her by finding all the Mini Peas. There are lots to spot!

BROCCOLI **CARROT** **CHILLI** **EVIL PEA**

SUPERTATO **TOMATO** **10 MINI PEAS**

Supertato's mighty headquarters – the Tato Tower!

Answers

SUPERTATO TO THE RESCUE!

SUPERMARKET MAYHEM!

LET'S PARTY!

RUN, VEGGIES, RUN!

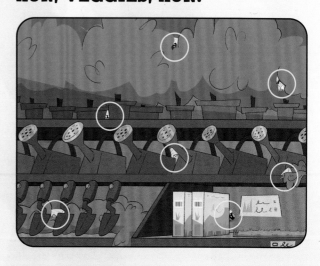

GAME ON!

PLANTS IN PERIL!

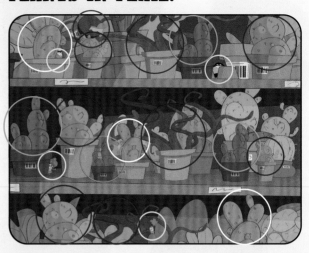

SUPER SPOTTER

DELI DANCE-OFF

SUPERMARKET SHOWDOWN

SUPERMARKET SING-A-LONG

DANGEROUS DOUGHNUTS

VEGGIES ASSEMBLE

THE BIG FREEZE

TATO TOWER TAKEOVER